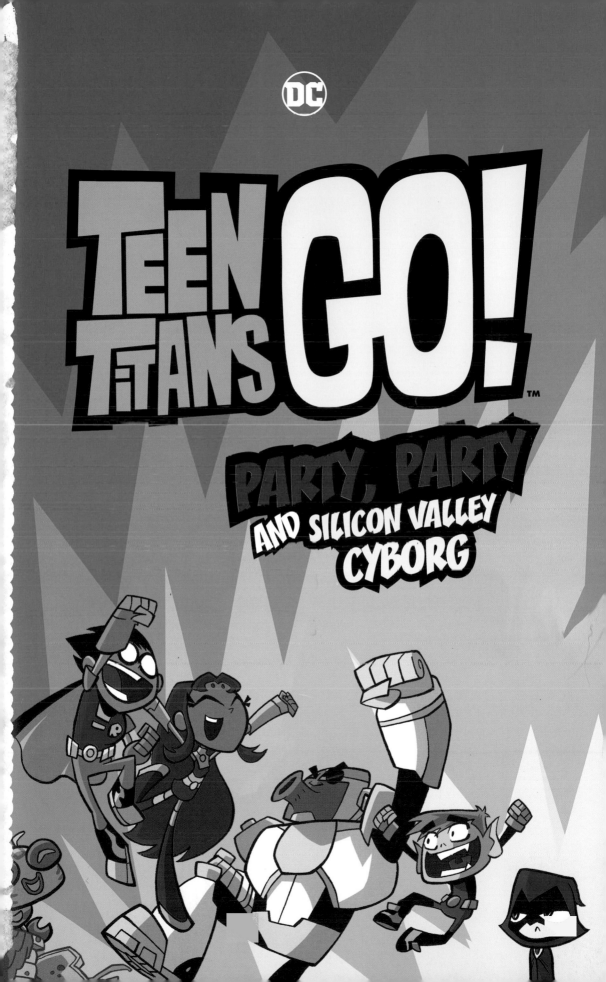

Raintree is an imprint of Capstone Global Library Limited, a company incorporated in England and Wales having its
registered office at 264 Banbury Road, Oxford, OX2 7DY – Registered company number: 6695582

www.raintree.co.uk
myorders@raintree.co.uk

Edited by Chris Harbo
Designed by Brann Garvey and Hilary Wacholz
Production by Kathy McColley
Originated by Capstone Global Library Ltd
Printed and bound in India

ISBN 978 1 4747 7324 9
22 21 20 19 18
10 9 8 7 6 5 4 3 2 1

British Library Cataloguing in Publication Data
A full catalogue record for this book is available from the British Library.

TEEN TITANS GO!™

AMY WOLFRAM   RICARDO SANCHEZ
WRITERS

JORGE CORONA   BEN BATES
ARTISTS

JEREMY LAWSON
COLOURIST

WES ABBOTT
LETTERER

DAN HIPP
COVER ARTIST

raintree
a Capstone company — publishers for children

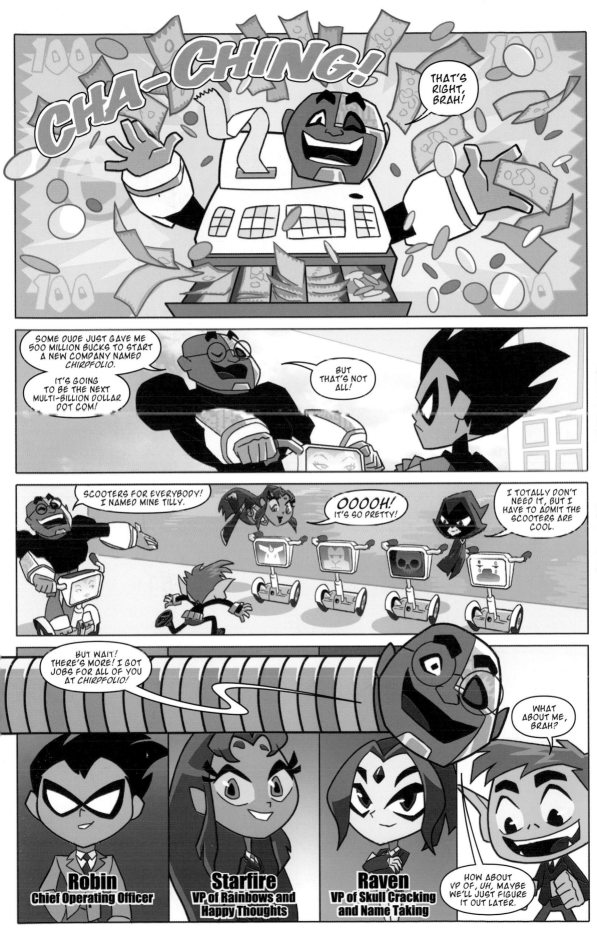

CREATORS

AMY WOLFRAM

Amy Wolfram is a comic book and television writer. She has written episodes for the animated TV series *Teen Titans*, *Legion of Super-Heroes* and *Teen Titans Go!*. In addition to the *Teen Titans Go!* comic book series, she has also written for *Teen Titans: Year One*.

RICARDO SANCHEZ

Ricardo Sanchez is a writer, Emmy-winning creator and executive producer. His comic book credits include *Batman: Legends of the Dark Knight*, *Resident Evil*, *RIFT: Telara Chronicles* and many others. When he's not writing comics, Ricardo maintains a vintage toy blog, drives 70's muscle cars and shops year round for Halloween decorations for his home in Redwood City, California, USA.

JORGE CORONA

Jorge Corona is a Venezuelan comic book artist who is well known for his all-ages fantasy-adventure series *Feathers* and his work on *Jim Henson's The Storyteller: Dragons*. In addition to *Teen Titans Go!*, he has also worked on *Batman Beyond*, *Justice League Beyond*, *We Are Robin*, *Goners* and many other comics.

BEN BATES

Ben Bates is a comic book illustrator, colourist and writer. In addition to *Teen Titans Go!*, he has also worked on *Teenage Mutant Ninja Turtles*, *Mega Man*, *My Little Pony* and many other comics.

GLOSSARY

advertising using words and pictures to encourage people to buy a product

cater provide food for a large group of people

celebrity relating to a famous person

CEO highest-ranking person in a company; short for Chief Executive Officer

croissant crescent-shaped French bread roll made from buttered layers of yeast dough

dignity quality that makes people worthy of honour or respect

dot com internet-based company

festivity activity that is part of a celebration

fortune large amount of money

gender sex of a person or creature (male or female)

genetic engineering inserting genes from one species into another species

inherit receive someone's property after they die

larva insect at the stage of development between an egg and a pupa when it looks like a worm

nourishment food that is necessary for growth

paradigm model

ritual action performed as part of a religious or social custom

sensitive relating to something that should be kept secret

stock option when a company gives its workers the option to buy shares (also known as stocks) at a reduced price. The ownership of a company is divided into many equal parts called shares. Shares can be bought by people as a way to make money over time.

transport something that carries someone from one place to another

vegetarian person who does not eat meat

VISUAL QUESTIONS & WRITING PROMPTS

1. Cyborg and Beast Boy suggest a number of interesting party themes. Think up your own unique party theme and write a paragraph describing what it would include.

2. Based on this panel, how do the party guests and hosts feel about each other? How do you know?

3. Flashbacks help readers understand details from a character's backstory. Based on this flashback, how does Starfire feel about the bathroom at Titan Tower and why?

4. What do you think happened to Robin just before this panel? Write a short paragraph describing the events that led him here.